MADAM&EVE

MADAMS are from MARS

MAIDS ARE FROM VENUS

by S.Francis, H. Dugmore & Rico

PENGUIN BOOKS

PENGUIN BOOKS

Published by the Penguin Group
27 Wrights Lane, London W8 5TZ, England
Viking Penguin, a division of Penguin Books USA Inc,
375 Hudson Street, New York, New York 10014, USA
Penguin Books Australia Ltd, Ringwood, Victoria, Australia
Penguin Books Canada Ltd, 10 Alcorn Avenue, Toronto, Ontario, Canada M4V 3B2
Penguin Books (NZ) Ltd, 182-190 Wairau Road, Auckland 10, New Zealand
Penguin Books (South Africa) (Pty) Ltd, 1A Eton Road, Parktown, South Africa 2193

Penguin Books (South Africa) (Pty) Ltd,
Registered Offices: Private Bag X14, Parkview 2122

First Published by Penguin Books 1997

ISBN 0 140 26656 9

Typesetting and reproduction by Boss Repro Centre
Printed and bound by Interpak, Natal

MADAM&EVE

"HIDE THE VACUUM CLEANER AND GET OUT THE OVEN MITTS!"
"Vibrant satire with praise and acclaim from all corners of South Africa."
-The Saturday Star

"THE COUNTRY'S BEST KNOWN CARTOON STRIP."
"... Plays on the absurdities of South African race relations."
-The Economist

"SOUTH AFRICA'S FAVOURITE TRILOGY OF TERROR."
"Madam & Eve, and the gin-swigging Mother Anderson keep going from strength to strength."
-Options Magazine

"BRILLIANT."
"... South Africa's number one cartoon strip has captured the hearts and funny bones of ordinary South Africans."
-The Sunday Times

"FIVE CHEERS FOR MADAM &EVE."
"South Africa's most successful cartoon strip has won the hearts of millions."
-The Mail & Guardian

"THEY DON'T COME MUCH BETTER THAN THIS."
"Consistently and hilariously funny."
-The Daily Dispatch

"A WHOLE LOT OF FUN!"
"... Madam & Eve has helped all South Africans laugh at themselves."
-The Eastern Province Herald

"A REFLECTION AND PART OF THE CULTURE."
"Madam & Eve are us."
-The Cape Argus

"MADAM & EVE..."
"A nation that laughs together."
-The Sunday Tribune

Other Madam & Eve books

Madam & Eve appears regularly in:

The Mail & Guardian, The Star, The Saturday Star, City Press,
The Eastern Province Herald, The Natal Mercury, The Natal Witness,
The Daily Dispatch, The Cape Times, The Diamond Fields Advertiser,
Die Volksblad, The Pretoria News, Zimbabwe Standard,
The S.A. Times, Fair Lady, Vodaworld, Student Life,
Ernie (Bladkompaniet A.S., Oslo) and Larson! (Atlantic Forlags AB, Stockholm)

To contact Madam & Eve:

POST: PO Box 94, WITS Post Office, 2050 South Africa
E-MAIL: madamandeve@pop.onwe.co.za
WORLD WIBE WEB: Visit Madam & Eve at the
Electronic Mail & Guardian's Web page: http://www.mg.co.za/mg/

8

11

I THINK YOU'RE RIGHT, MOM. EVE DEFINITELY DISCOVERED OUR HIDDEN VIDEO CAMERA.

ISN'T THIS GREAT?! WE HAVE MADAM'S HOUSE ALL TO OURSELVES!

02:46:13:58

WAIT-- LOOK OUT! GIANT DINOSAURS!!

02:48:39:43

ROARR!! AAAH! HELP!

SPECIAL EFFECTS! SHE ADDED SPECIAL EFFECTS!!

ARE YOU READY TO GO?

YES... BUT FIRST LET ME TURN ON OUR HIDDEN VIDEO CAMERA.

02:10:13:58

HEH-HEH. WAIT TILL EVE FINDS OUT WE'RE SECRETLY TAPING EVERYTHING SHE DOES WHEN WE LEAVE THE HOUSE.

02:11:39:43

WON'T SHE BE SURPRISED!

HEE-HEE!

02:12:57:04

DON'T GO AWAY! WE'LL BE BACK WITH MORE OF "EVE'S PUPPET PLAYHOUSE"... AFTER THIS.

ANYTHING GOOD ON TV?

02:10:13:58

02:11:39:43

02:12:57:04

WELL... SO MUCH FOR THE "HIDDEN VIDEO CAMERA TO SPY ON THE MAID" IDEA.

HELLO. I'M FROM THE **CENSUS BOARD**. MIND IF I COME IN FOR A FEW MINUTES?

OF COURSE! THIS IS MY **MAID**... AND THIS IS MY **MOTHER**.

...I'M NOT **REALLY** HER MOTHER. SHE WON ME IN A **POKER GAME**.

FOR A HEAVY GUY, HE SURE RUNS FAST.

READY?   READY.

REMEMBER-- ONE HAND OF POKER. IF I WIN, MY DAUGHTER **STOPS** BEING THE **MAID** AND THINGS GO BACK TO NORMAL.

DEAL THE CARDS.

MADAM & Eve

BY S.FRANCIS, H.DUGMORE & RICO

KNOCK!
KNOCK!
KNOCK!
KNOCK!

THIS BETTER BE GOOD! IT'S AFTER TWO IN THE MORNING!! WHO IS IT?!!

IT'S JAMES SMALL.

AND THERE I WAS...RUNNING FOR THE TRY-LINE. I LOOK UP... AND WHO DO I SEE? JONAH LOMU HEADING RIGHT FOR ME! SO I CUT TO THE LEFT AND...

HEY!! ARE YOU GUYS PAYING ATTENTION OR WHAT?!!

I'M TELLING YOU GREAT RUGBY STORIES HERE!

JAMES... IT'S AFTER TWO IN THE MORNING. DON'T YOU HAVE A GAME TOMORROW?

WHO CARES?! IT'S PARTY TIME! GOT ANY BEER IN THE FRIDGE?!

MOM. WE'RE GOING TO BED. SEE IF YOU CAN GET RID OF HIM.

NO PROBLEM.

PARTY! PARTY! PARTY!

HEY! GREAT LIQUOR CABINET!! WHO DRINKS ALL THIS GIN?!!

AND IN OTHER NEWS, SPRINGBOK WINGER JAMES SMALL WAS ONCE AGAIN OUT PARTYING LAST NIGHT TILL AFTER TWO IN THE MORNING.

ACCORDING TO REPORTS, RIDING ON THE BACK OF HIS MOTORCYCLE WAS AN UNIDENTIFIED EIGHTY YEAR-OLD WOMAN.

MADAM & EVE

BY S. FRANCIS, H. DUGMORE & RICO

DR. ZUMA...THE SOUTH AFRICAN PEOPLE REFUSE TO BE PUT OFF ANY LONGER. WE NEED TO **KNOW** THE IDENTITY OF THE **SECRET MYSTERY DONOR!**

OKAY. I'LL TELL YOU.

GOOD. WHO IS IT?

ELVIS.

ELVIS? ELVIS PRESLEY?!!

YES! HE'S NOT ONLY **ALIVE**... HE **LOVED** SARAFINA II **SO MUCH**, HE WANTS TO DONATE 10,5 MILLION!

MINISTER, ARE YOU DELIBERATELY MISLEADING THIS COMMITTEE?!

OKAY, OKAY. DID I SAY ELVIS? IT WASN'T ELVIS.

GOOD. NOW WE'RE GETTING SOMEWHERE.

...IT WAS **ALIENS**.

ILLEGAL ALIENS?

SPACE ALIENS! THEY ABDUCTED ME AND PERFORMED MEDICAL EXPERIMENTS. IN RETURN, THEY OFFERED TO BAIL OUT SARAFINA II.

MINISTER, PLEASE!

OKAY, OKAY. YOU WIN. IT JUST SO HAPPENS I HAVE THE **IDENTITY** OF THE MYSTERY DONOR WRITTEN **RIGHT HERE** ON THIS PIECE OF PAPER...

OOPS. I GUESS MY DOG ACCIDENTALLY ATE IT.

MINISTER! WE DEMAND THAT YOU REVEAL THE MYSTERY DONOR'S NAME IMMEDIATELY!

WHY DON'T YOU ASK HIM YOURSELF? HE'S **RIGHT BEHIND** YOU!

MADE YOU LOOK.

28

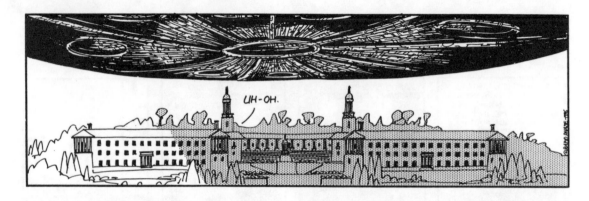

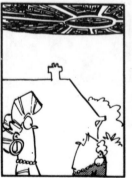

MADAM & EVE

BY S. FRANCIS, H. DUGMORE & RICO

AND IN OTHER NEWS, THE SABC HAS HIRED OVER 3000 PART-TIME EMPLOYEES TO INVESTIGATE **PIRATE VIEWERS** WHO DON'T PAY THEIR TV-LICENSES.

CAN YOU **BELIEVE** THIS?! WHO WOULD RAT OUT THEIR OWN FRIENDS AND FAMILY FOR MONEY?!

EVERYONE FREEZE!!
FREE-LANCE SABC TV-LICENSE INVESTIGATOR!!

MOM-- YOU DIDN'T!

SORRY. NOTHING PERSONAL... IT'S JUST BUSINESS.

LET'S GO! UP AGAINST THE WALL! ASSUME THE POSITION!

MOM! HOW CAN YOU TURN IN YOUR OWN DAUGHTER FOR A LOUSY COMMISSION?!

AHA! WHAT'S THIS?! A TV REMOTE CONTROL!

I...I NEVER SAW IT BEFORE IN MY LIFE!

SURE. THAT'S WHAT THEY ALL SAY! LISTEN...WE CAN MAKE THIS **EASY**... OR WE GO **DOWNTOWN** TO AUCKLAND PARK. IT'S UP TO YOU.

OKAY! YOU WIN! I'LL PAY MY LICENSE FEE! I'LL WRITE YOU A CHEQUE!

GOOD.

:SQUAWK: AGENT SILVER FOX TO BASE. I GOT ANOTHER PERPETRATOR...MY COVER'S BLOWN HERE. I'LL BE NEEDING A **NEW** IDENTITY.

ROGER, SILVER FOX.

SO. ANYTHING GOOD ON TV?

34

REMEMBER, MOM. THE DOCTOR SAID THAT EVE'S **MEMORY** COULD **COME BACK** AT ANY TIME. WE'VE GOT TO BE PATIENT.

HELLO, EVE. DO YOU REMEMBER US? I'M GWEN... AND THIS IS EDITH.

I'M GETTING HUNGRY, GWEN AND EDITH. HOW ABOUT SOME LUNCH?

BE RIGHT BACK.

WITH ANY LUCK, I CAN STRETCH THIS **AMNESIA** THING FOR AT LEAST TWO WEEKS.

VACUUMING CARPETS AND WASHING AND DRYING...

IRONING JACKETS AND COOKING AND FRYING...

WIPING UP DUSTBALLS...

...AND DIRTY SINK RINGS...

...THESE ARE A FEW OF YOUR FAVOURITE THINGS.

SORRY. CAN'T REMEMBER ANYTHING.

LISTEN TO THIS. "AMNESIA VICTIMS OFTEN REGAIN THEIR MEMORY WITH ANOTHER **BLOW** TO THE HEAD."

HIT EVE ON THE HEAD? I COULD NEVER DO THAT!

MORNING GWEN! MORNING EDITH!

SO. WHAT'S FOR **BREAKFAST**?

OH GOOD. ...FRIED EGGS?

40

He arrived
from the
future...

To change
the past...

Persistent,
Relentless,
and
Unstoppable...

TERMINATOR III

The Last Hope.

Coming soon
to a theatre near you.

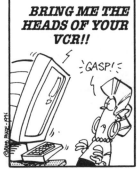

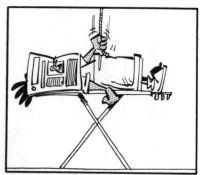

BY S. FRANCIS, H. DUGMORE & RICO

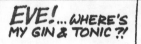

EVE!...WHERE'S MY GIN & TONIC?!

EVE!...WHERE'S MY GIN & TONIC?!

ISN'T HE BEAUTIFUL, MOM? IT'S MARGE'S PARROT. I TOLD HER I'D TAKE CARE OF HIM TILL SHE COMES BACK FROM HOLIDAY.

:AWK!: EVE! WHERE'S MY GIN & TONIC?!

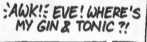

:AWK: EVE! WHERE'S MY GIN & TONIC?!

JUST BE CAREFUL. WHATEVER THE PARROT HEARS, IT REPEATS OVER AND OVER AGAIN. SO WATCH WHAT YOU SAY OUT LOUD.

MIELLLIES!!

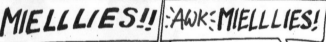

:AWK: MIELLLIES!

MIELLLLIES!!

MIELLLIES!!

:AWK: MIELLLIES! HELP! SHE'S CHOKING ME! MIELLLIES! :AWK: HELP! SHE'S CHOKING ME! MIELLIES! :SQUAWK!!:

http://www.mg.co.za/mg/

© RAPID PHASE 1997

84

MADAM & Eve

BY S. FRANCIS, H. DUGMORE & RICO

NOW THAT THE NEW LABOUR LAW IS IN EFFECT, I TOOK THE LIBERTY OF DRAWING UP A SMALL CONTRACT FOR YOU TO SIGN.

OKAY. LET'S SKIP TO PAGE SEVEN.

FLIP FLIP FLIP FLIP FLIP.

YOUR...

...COFFEE...

...MADAM.

YOU CAN **GO SLOW** AS MUCH AS YOU WANT. I'M STILL NOT SIGNING THAT CONTRACT!

MADAM & Eve

BY S. FRANCIS, H. DUGMORE & RICO

EVERYONE! I'M BACK FROM THE FLEA MARKET!

JUST WAIT TILL YOU SEE ALL THE GREAT THINGS I BOUGHT!

LOOK AT THIS! A GENUINE AFRICAN COWHIDE SHIELD WITH A SPEAR AND CLUB!

WAIT TILL YOU SEE THIS! A HANDMADE BICYCLE MADE ENTIRELY OUT OF WIRE!

... A GIANT WROUGHT-IRON CANDLE-STICK HOLDER!

... A STATUE OF AN AFRICAN HEAD WITH A BEARD!

...A PAINTING OF FOUR DOGS PLAYING POKER.

AND THIS IS MY FAVOURITE! A BUNCH OF LITTLE BLACK GUYS PLAYING INSTRUMENTS!

SO, WHERE SHOULD I PUT IT ALL?

YOUR ROOM.

REALLY? YOU WOULDN'T MIND?

MADAM & Eve

BY S. FRANCIS, H. DUGMORE & RICO

DINNER'S READY, EVERYONE!

OH BOY, POTATOES.

HOLD IT, EVE, YOU FORGOT THE GRAVY.

I'LL GET IT.

NO. I'LL GET IT.

BUMF!

WAIT A MINUTE. I'LL GO LEFT, YOU GO RIGHT.

GOOD IDEA.

CRASH!

POP

SCRAMBLED TOFU?!! ...FOR BREAKFAST?!!

MADAM, SAYS WE'RE ALL GOING ON CRASH DIETS.

MADAM & Eve

BY S. FRANCIS, H. DUGMORE & RICO

MOM! COME HERE! I WANT YOU TO SEE THIS!

I COME IN HERE -- AND WHAT DO I FIND? EVE ON TOP OF THE IRONING BOARD!!

DON'T I PAY HER GOOD MONEY?! AM I AN UNREASONABLE EMPLOYER?!

YOU'D THINK SHE COULD DO A SIMPLE CHORE LIKE IRONING -- BUT NO, SHE WANTS TO LIE ON TOP OF THE IRONING BOARD!

MAYBE SHE HAS A GOOD REASON.

A GOOD REASON?!! WHAT COULD POSSIBLY BE A GOOD REASON WHY ANYONE WOULD LIE ON TOP OF AN IRONING BOARD?!!

PARKTOWN PRAWN.

92

93

MADAM & Eve

TWAS THE NIGHT BEFORE CHRISTMAS, AND AT THE NORTH POLE, A *VISITOR* PITCHED FROM OUT OF THE COLD.

BY S. FRANCIS, H. DUGMORE & RICO

"I'M HERE FROM "SOUTH AFRICA," ...HE SAID WITH A GRIN, "I'VE GOT TO SEE SANTA-- NOW PLEASE LET ME IN!"

"FATHER CHRISTMAS," HE SAID. "IF I MAY BE SO BOLD-- THIS "SLEIGH-THING" IS TIRED... YOUR ACT'S GETTING OLD!"

"I'M A WRITER-PRODUCER, I'VE HAD MANY HITS. WHAT YOU NEED IS A PLAY WITH GLAMOUR AND GLITZ."

"WE'LL TOUR THE WHOLE WORLD ON HUGE FLATBED TRUCKS! WE'LL CHARGE MONEY FOR TICKETS! WE'LL BRING IN THE BUCKS!"

"WITH ELVES IN THE CHORUS AND REINDEER THAT DANCE! "SANTAFINA"-- WE'LL CALL IT! IT'S YOUR BIG CHANCE!"

THIS SOUNDS MOST EXPENSIVE, HOW MUCH IS THE BILL?

WELL, NORMALLY LOTS! BUT FOR YOU-- 14 MILL!

THE ELVES SMILED AND GIGGLED. THE REINDEER MADE MERRY, AND THEN SANTA LAUGHED LIKE A BOWL FULL OF JELLY.

PAY 14 MILLION?!... IS THAT WHAT IT'S WORTH?! THERE'S NO ONE SO STUPID ON THE FACE OF THIS EARTH!

AND WITH THAT, OLD ST. NICK GOT INTO HIS SLEIGH, AND DROPPED THE MAN OFF ON HIS WAY TO SA.

AND THEY HEARD HIM EXCLAIM AS HE DROVE OUT OF SIGHT--

"PEACE ON EARTH TO YOU ALL! MERRY CHRISTMAS, GOOD NIGHT!"

CENSORED!

△
V L

This Cartoon Panel contains scenes of Extreme Violence and Foul Language.

EVE! WHY IS IT EVERY TIME YOU CLEAN THE HOUSE, YOU PUT THINGS BACK IN A **DIFFERENT** PLACE?!

I'VE TOLD YOU A THOUSAND TIMES! THE SALT AND PEPPER SHAKERS GO IN THE **TOP** CUPBOARD!

AND YOU **KNOW** MOM GOES IN THE TV ROOM!

MADAM & Eve

VED S.FRANCIS, H.DUGMØRE & RICO

Editor's Note:

The creators of Madam & Eve are on vacation.

However, since Madam & Eve is enjoyed all over the world, we are reprinting a cartoon recently published in Denmark.

The Danish Newspapers have kindly provided English subtitles.

EVE! TÆNK SÅ UD FRA DET ØRGE VAKUUM PÅ ER DERES **VIKING** HODE.

EVE! HOW MANY TIMES HAVE I TOLD YOU NOT TO WEAR YOUR VIKING HELMET WHEN YOU SUCK UP THE DUST!

MIELLLIES!!

ØH NEJ, MÅSKE DE AFRIKANSKE FRUE AT BLOT DU VÅLGFORDNEDE!

OH NO! IT IS THE AFRICAN LADY WHO SELLS THE YELLOW VEGETABLES.

IKKE VIRKER BÅD ER DE FØRST DU MINE PÅ MIG LØNFORHØJELSE.

I WILL NOW ANNOY HER WITH MY WOODEN WEAPON!

TWANG!

ØW!! HÅR-HÅR!

TWANG! | OW! | HA-HA.

ALTSÅ MADAM! SYDAFRIKANSKE KRIMINALITETEN!

LOOK MADAM! SOUTH AFRICAN CRIMINALS!

HÅNDE SÅDAN MERE RØLIG. JEG DRONNING ØR **VOLVO** KULESKØRE!

PUT YOUR ARMS IN THE SKY. WE WISH TO STEAL YOUR NEW VOLVO.

JEG HVONÅR MIG SKØNT TRYG FORSLAG **NELSON MANDELA**!

~GISP!~

GASP!

IF YOU DO, WE WILL BE FORCED TO TELL NELSON MANDELA.

ALTSÅ! SIG VÆRE FØRSTE AT VÅSKEN JEG HVAD SÅ LEBENDIGEN.

LOOK! THEY ARE RETREATING QUICKLY. WE ARE SAFE.

EVE! DER GIN OG TONIC HOVEDRETTEN SÅ **FORTABT**!

ØH NØØJ! JEG GJORDE DEN SLIPPET OPFØRTE SIG TAGELSE!

EVE! THE GIN & TONIC CONTAINER IS EMPTY! | OH NO! MY MIND SLIPPED TO PURCHASE SOME MORE !

SYDAFRIKA ER DU LÆGGE SPØRGSMÅL SIN LAND.

HÅR-HÅR HÅR-HÅR!

SOUTH AFRICA IS A MOST AMUSING COUNTRY. | HA-HA-HA HA-HA-HA!

MADAM & Eve

BY S. FRANCIS, H. DUGMORE & RICO

MADAMS ANONYMOUS

HELLO. MY NAME IS NONCEBA.

AND I'M... ≈CHOKE≈ ... A MADAM.

HI NONCEBA!!

IT SEEMED LIKE ALL MY FRIENDS HAD DOMESTIC WORKERS. THEY TOLD ME... "TRY IT -- YOU'LL LIKE IT!" ... AND SO I DID!

GASP

AT FIRST I JUST EXPERIMENTED... I HAD THE MAID COME IN JUST TUESDAYS AND THURSDAYS...

UH-HUH!

YEBO!

BUT IT WASN'T ENOUGH! I NEEDED THE HOUSE CLEANED EVERY DAY! AND BEFORE LONG... I WAS HOOKED! I HIRED A FULL-TIME LIVE-IN MAID!

I HAVEN'T WASHED ONE OF MY OWN DISHES IN THREE MONTHS!

OH NO! WE'VE BEEN THERE!

≈SOB≈ IT GETS WORSE. I EVEN MAKE HER WORK OVERTIME WITH NO PAY!

GASP

≈SOB≈

THANK YOU, NONCEBA. THAT TOOK A LOT OF COURAGE.

AND NOW, I'D LIKE YOU TO WELCOME OUR SPECIAL GUEST TO HELP US DEAL WITH THE GUILT... EXPERIENCED MADAM, EDITH ANDERSON.

CLAP CLAP CLAP CLAP CLAP CLAP CLAP CLAP

OKAY. EVERYONE HOLD UP YOUR TV REMOTE CONTROL AND YOUR GIN & TONIC.

I WROTE A POEM FOR SCHOOL.

THAT'S NICE.

I CALL IT "ODE TO A GIN & TONIC."

GIN & TONIC... IT LOOKS SO BUBBLY. AND WHEN YOU DRINK IT, YOUR LEGS GO RUBBERY.

YOU READ THAT TO YOUR CLASS ?!

YEAH. MY TEACHER SAYS SHE WANTS TO HAVE A TALK WITH YOU.

AND NOW... WE CONTINUE WITH OUR TOP TWENTY GOLDEN OLDIE COUNTDOWN..

...COMING IN AT NUMBER TWELVE--

...THAT, OF COURSE, WAS THE BEACH BOYS... WITH "SURFIN' USA."

MADAM & EVE

BY S. FRANCIS, H. DUGMORE & RICO

From humble beginnings...

He built an empire.

He had many enemies.

But when they cried "Nepotism", it was time to *fight*.

Warner Bros Pictures presents

One Man's fight for freedom of speech ...and the right to hire his family.

AND IN OTHER NEWS, **PRINCESS DIANA** SLIPPED INTO SOUTH AFRICA THIS WEEK.

APART FROM A VISIT WITH NELSON MANDELA, **DI** HAS SO FAR MANAGED TO AVOID PHOTOGRAPHERS AND THE PRESS.

WHERE IS DI? NO ONE KNOWS. BUT RUMOURS PERSIST THAT SHE'S STAYING AT A PRIVATE HOME.

SO. WHAT ATTRACTED YOU TO PRINCE CHARLES?

HIS EARS.

HELLO MARGE? YOU'RE NOT GOING TO **BELIEVE** THIS.

GUESS WHO'S STAYING WITH US WHILE SHE'S IN SOUTH AFRICA? **PRINCESS DI!**

NO, I'M **NOT** JOKING! SHE'S IN MY LOUNGE RIGHT NOW TALKING TO EVE ABOUT SOUTH AFRICAN POLITICS AND WORLD AFFAIRS.

OKAY. CAPTAIN JAMES HEWITT...YES OR NO?

ON A SCALE FROM ONE TO TEN?

PRINCESS DI... I'D LIKE YOU TO MEET SOMEONE VERY SPECIAL...

AAAAAAH!! SHE FOUND ME!! KEEP HER AWAY!! KEEP BACK!!

THIS IS WEIRD, MOM. DI SAYS YOU LOOK EXACTLY LIKE HER MOTHER IN LAW!

REALLY? I LOOK LIKE THE QUEEN OF ENGLAND?

MY LOYAL SUBJECTS...

AAAAH!! NO! STAY BACK!

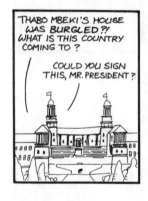

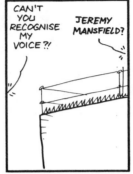

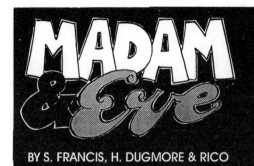

CASABLANCA

Starring
Humphrey Boesak

BY S. FRANCIS, H. DUGMORE & RICO

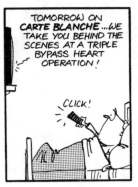

THE SPECIAL EDITION TRUTH COMMISSION CALLS THE NEXT WITNESS SEEKING AMNESTY... LUKE SKYWALKER.

MR. SKYWALKER... IT'S ALLEGED YOU BLEW UP THE DEATH STAR. WHAT WE NEED TO KNOW IS WHERE DID IT HAPPEN... AND WHEN?

CAN I CONSULT WITH MY ATTORNEY?

BSSST. BSSST.

BEEP. BEEP. BOOOP! DAWHEEP!

...A LONG TIME AGO IN A GALAXY FAR FAR AWAY.

SPECIFICS! WE WANT SPECIFICS!

THE TRUTH COMMISSION IS GETTING IMPATIENT MR. SKYWALKER.

WHAT WAS THE QUESTION, AGAIN?

WHEN YOU BLEW UP THE DEATH STAR AND DEFEATED THE EMPIRE... DID YOU DO IT ALONE?!

NO. THE FORCE WAS WITH ME.

THE FORCE?!

AHA! THE THIRD FORCE!! NOW WE'RE GETTING SOMEWHERE!

A long time ago In a supermarket far, far away...

SPAR WARS

138

MADAM & Eve

BY S.FRANCIS, H.DUGMORE & RICO

...AND IN OTHER NEWS, THE RESULT OF THE ANC WOMEN'S LEAGUE PRESIDENTIAL ELECTION ARE FINALLY IN. THE WINNER IS... WINNIE MADIKIZELA MANDELA!

GROAN ≡ SIGH ≡ AARRGH!

OKAY. WHO-EVER PICKS THE SHORT STRAW HAS TO TELL YOU-KNOW-WHO.

COME IN.

KNOCK KNOCK

MORNING, MISTER PRESIDENT.

GOOD MORNING!

HEY--HOW ABOUT BAFANA BAFANA? DID YOU SEE THE GAME?

YES. BUT I'M UH, RATHER BUSY RIGHT NOW...

THEN LET ME GET TO THE POINT, SIR. I HAVE GOOD NEWS AND BAD NEWS.

WHICH DO YOU WANT FIRST?

THE BAD NEWS.

...YOUR EX-WIFE WAS JUST ELECTED PRESIDENT OF THE ANC WOMEN'S LEAGUE.

QUICKLY! WHAT'S THE GOOD NEWS?

IT COULD HAVE BEEN DOCTOR ZUMA!

SIR?...MISTER PRESIDENT? ARE YOU OKAY? ...SIR?

144

MADAM -- ARE YOU THROWING OUT THIS OLD TYPEWRITER?

YES. WHY?

I'LL TAKE IT! I'VE ALWAYS WONDERED IF I COULD WRITE THE GREAT SOUTH AFRICAN NOVEL.

HEE-HEE. THE GREAT SOUTH AFRICAN NOVEL.

THIS I GOTTA SEE.

"THE MADAM FROM HELL" An unauthorised Biography

I'LL BE BACK SOON. I'M GOING TO THE SHOP. I'M OUT OF PAPER.

STILL WORKING ON THE GREAT SOUTH AFRICAN NOVEL, I SEE.

YEP. SHE'S BEEN TYPING ALL NIGHT.

"MAID TO ORDER" ...THE STORY OF A DOMESTIC WORKER AND HER GROSSLY UNFAIR EMPLOYER."

I'LL KILL HER.

I CAN'T BELIEVE EVE'S WRITING A NOVEL ABOUT US! DID SHE USE OUR REAL NAMES?

NOT EXACTLY.

...INSTEAD OF GWEN, THE MADAM'S NAME IS GWINITH. INSTEAD OF EVE, THE MAID'S NAME IS "EVA".

IS THERE A MOTHER FROM ENGLAND IN THE BOOK? WHAT'S HER NAME?

GINNY.

I'LL KILL HER.

EVE... DO YOU THINK YOU'VE BEEN TOO HARSH ON GWEN IN YOUR BOOK?

NOT AT ALL, FELICIA. SHE WAS DEFINITELY THE **MADAM FROM HELL.**

EXCUSE ME, BUT THE REASON I AGREED TO BE ON THIS TV SHOW WAS TO GET A FAIR HEARING... TO **CLEAR** MY NAME!

RIGHT. LET'S SEE WHAT OUR STUDIO AUDIENCE THINKS!

MADAM FROM HELL!

MADAM FROM HELL!

MADAM FROM HELL!

MADAM FROM HELL!

IF SHE EVER FINISHES THAT BOOK, WE'RE IN BIG TROUBLE.

I'M SORRY, MS. SISULU, BUT AFTER CAREFUL CONSIDERATION WE HAVE TO TURN YOU DOWN. WE **CAN'T** PUBLISH YOUR NOVEL.

WHAT? WHY?!

A "MADAM FROM HELL" WHO DOES NOTHING BUT GO SHOPPING, WATCH TV AND THEN ACCUSES THE MAID OF STEALING THE COFFEE AND SUGAR?

... AN EIGHTY YEAR OLD "MOTHER FROM ENGLAND" WHO DRINKS FIVE GIN & TONICS A DAY AND THEN CHASES MIELIE LADIES AROUND THE BLOCK?!

I'M AFRAID THESE CHARACTERS ARE JUST TOO **UNBELIEVABLE.**

153

MADAM & Eve

BY S. FRANCIS, H. DUGMORE & RICO

OUR GUEST TONIGHT IS NEWLY-APPOINTED *CEO* OF THE SOUTH AFRICAN POLICE SERVICE, MEYER KAHN.

MISTER KAHN...AS THE FORMER HEAD OF SOUTH AFRICAN BREWERIES, WHAT'S THE FIRST THING YOU'LL DO AS CHIEF OF POLICE?

DRAUGHT MORE COPS! I WANT MORE POLICE AVAILABLE ON TAP!

AND ANOTHER THING: THERE'LL BE *NO MORE* OFFICERS TRAVELLING IN *PAIRS*. FROM NOW ON, PATROLS WILL BE AVAILABLE IN HANDY, ECONOMIC *SIX-PACKS*.

UH, WHAT ABOUT THE CRIMINALS THEMSELVES, SIR?

I WANT TO PUT A *CAP* ON CRIME. THERE'LL BE LOTS OF *MUG SHOTS*!!

AND THAT'S NOT ALL! ANYONE CAUGHT *FERMENTING* VIOLENCE WILL BE IN BIG TROUBLE!

...DON'T YOU MEAN... "*FOMENTING*" VIOLENCE?

YES!...FOAM! A GOOD HEAD OF FOAM IS VERY IMPORTANT!

UH, MISTER KAHN. SOME PEOPLE MIGHT SAY THAT YOU'VE SPENT *TOO LONG* IN THE *BEER INDUSTRY* TO UNDERSTAND LAW ENFORCEMENT.

ABSOLUTELY NOT! POLICING IS LIKE *ANY BUSINESS*! I'LL *HOP* TO IT AND *GULP* DOWN THE CHALLENGE! I'LL SEND A *CLEAR, RICH AMBER* MESSAGE TO ALL CRIMINALS!

WHAT ABOUT YOUR RELATIONSHIP WITH COMMISSIONER FIVAZ? HOW IS IT?

NOT SO GOOD. RIGHT NOW WE'RE AT *LAGERHEADS*.

UH... DON'T YOU MEAN... "*LOGGERHEADS*", SIR?

DAMMIT, MAN! ALL I'M SAYING IS THAT THERE'S TROUBLE *BREWING* AND WE'VE GOT TO OPEN ALL THE *BOTTLENECKS*!

IF YOU LEND ME FIVE RAND, I'LL EASILY BE ABLE TO PAY YOU BACK NEXT WEEK.

SURE YOU WILL.

FINE! IF YOU DON'T BELIEVE ME, READ THIS. IT CAME IN THE POST TODAY.

"CONGRATULATIONS. YOU MAY HAVE ALREADY WON A MILLION RANDS."

YOU SEE? I MAY HAVE ALREADY WON A MILLION RANDS AND YOU'RE WORRIED ABOUT A LOUSY FIVE BUCKS?!

YEP. ACCORDING TO THIS LETTER, I MAY HAVE ALREADY WON A MILLION RANDS.

WHICH RAISES A FEW QUESTIONS: WHERE DID I WIN IT, WHEN DID I WIN IT, AND WHY DIDN'T THEY COME AND NOTIFY ME RIGHT AWAY INSTEAD OF SENDING A LETTER?

EXACTLY! SO WHAT DOES THAT TELL YOU?!

...THAT WHOEVER OWES ME A MILLION BUCKS HAS A LOT OF EXPLAINING TO DO.

BY THE WAY. I'M A MILLIONAIRE.

MMM HMM...

IT'S TRUE! LISTEN TO WHAT CAME IN THE POST! "CONGRATULATIONS! YOU MAY HAVE ALREADY WON A MILLION RAND!"

"MAY HAVE!" THAT'S HOW THEY TRICK YOU! YOU MAY HAVE WON-- OR YOU MAY HAVE NOT!!

THAT'S OKAY. I CAN LIVE WITH A FIFTY-FIFTY CHANCE.

MIELLIES!!

BONK

WHIRRRR

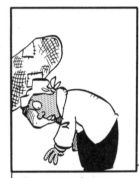

RATTLE RATTLE RATTLE

CLICK WHIRR...

MIELLLIES!

AND WE'LL RETURN WITH MORE ON THIS INCREDIBLE NEW DEVELOPMENT FROM THE MARS PATHFINDER MISSION IN JUST A MOMENT.

171